IN MY
Words

*An Interactive Self-Help Guide,
That Outlines, The Five "L's" To
Living A Full Life.*

LAKESA MCGRAW

PREAMBLE

Every single day we battle with work-life balance or the mere forgetfulness of self. It is time to remember that life is to be lived. Being held to unrealistic expectations and losing yourself was never apart of the plan. It is possible to take care of your responsibilities and still live a full life, remembering the pieces of the puzzle that were uniquely designed to create the best version of you.

FIVE "L'S" TO LIVING A
Full Life

If you are ready to regain control and refocus, grab a notebook and a pen, it's time to put your oxygen mask on and give life to you, your dreams and goals.

Breathe!

Life

In life, the cards that you are dealt aren't always a winning hand. However, what we can do is change the game, shuffle those same cards, and create a strategy to come out on top, a winner.

Our experiences have shaped our lives. We find ourselves responding to life, trauma, baggage, pain, frustration, love, and happiness; all from an emotional place, we do this because we haven't been taught to do otherwise.

66

Don't rob yourself of potential opportunities, simply because you don't want to do the work or change your behavior to get there.

If you continue on the path that you are on, you will never accomplish the goals that you have set out for yourself.

You have to be willing to make the time to do the work, to truly see the results.

FIVE "L'S" TO LIVING A
Full Life

SHARE YOUR THOUGHTS

"

You'll learn that trying to be everything to everyone, leaves you little time to give anything to yourself.

While you are trying to stand in the gap for them, you do not realize how you are being drained of your time and energy; both being things that you can't get back.

Always choose you!

SHARE YOUR THOUGHTS

"

If your heart and intentions are pure, you'll never lack the essentials needed to live a full life.

SHARE YOUR THOUGHTS

66

Pride Will Choke You And Keep You From
Mending Broken Relationships. Apologize
And Make Things Right With The People
Who Are Most Important In Life.

FIVE "L'S" TO LIVING A
Full Life

SHARE YOUR THOUGHTS

66

Why would you let the fear of tomorrow, overshadow the beauty of today?

SHARE YOUR THOUGHTS

66

There is a light inside of you that deserves to shine. Do you even remember what makes you great?

SHARE YOUR THOUGHTS

"

If you ever find yourself trapped in a box, I hope that it is a box without a lid, because the sky is truly the limit.

Remember that the only person who can change your life is you.

SHARE YOUR THOUGHTS

"

Every day won't be a good day. Sometimes you are going to wish for a reset simply because life happens. However, even when tough times arise, you have the option to either overcome it or be swept away by the tide.

Remember that your faith should always be bigger than obstacles you may face.

SHARE YOUR THOUGHTS

"

Be intentional today and every day. You wouldn't waste time driving a car around without a destination, so don't live your life that way.

Put in the coordinates and don't stop until you get there. Even if you have to make a stop for fuel, know that none of us can run off of an empty tank, and pouring back into you is necessary; keep driving.

FIVE "L'S" TO LIVING A
Full Life

SHARE YOUR THOUGHTS

"

To get the results that you want, you have to be willing to do the work; because if you're going to believe in anyone, always believe in yourself.

When was the last time you trusted your instinct?

FIVE "L'S" TO LIVING A
Full Life

SHARE YOUR THOUGHTS

66

Don't let the grind, keep you from celebrating the small wins.

Look back over your life and list the things that you've accomplished. Give yourself the kudos that you deserve.

SHARE YOUR THOUGHTS

66

Don't be afraid to tell your story. Your story is filled with the test that molded your testimony. You would have never become who you are without it.

You never know... Your testimony could be the one thing that changes someone else's life.

FIVE "L'S" TO LIVING A
Full Life

SHARE YOUR THOUGHTS

"

Don't let anyone trick you out of your blessings. You know where you're going, so stop waiting on the blind to validate your vision.

If you wouldn't use a broken compass for directions, then you shouldn't use broken mirrors to reflect your future.

SHARE YOUR THOUGHTS

66

Humility does not mean that you have to shrink away. It simply means that you should always show gratitude for the journey that led you here.

Appreciate your climb, but don't ignore the heights that you've been blessed enough to reach along your journey.

FIVE "L'S" TO LIVING A
Full Life

SHARE YOUR THOUGHTS

66

Don't focus so much on what "they say,"
pay attention to how they treat you.

With that in mind, make sure that you are
mindful of how you treat others as well.

FIVE "L'S" TO LIVING A
Full Life

SHARE YOUR THOUGHTS

Love

We all struggle with love. Either we struggle with not receiving it, showing it or accepting the fact that we deserve it. Regardless of your struggle, one indisputable fact is that life is not worth living without it.

It is time to be released and open your heart again because love is waiting on the other side of your fear.

"

Love yourself enough to become healthy in every aspect.

What are some negative habits that you could change to become an even greater version of yourself?

FIVE "L'S" TO LIVING A
Full Life

HOW DO YOU FEEL?

66

There is beauty in your flaws.

Do you even know what makes you
beautiful?

FIVE "L'S" TO LIVING A
Full Life

HOW DO YOU FEEL?

66

Love is an action word. It is not just what
you say, but it is how you show up.

How are you showing up and who is showing
up for you?

HOW DO YOU FEEL?

SELF-HELP
Guide

"

There is nothing more important than the love of self and the boundaries you set. Make a declaration today to revoke access to your heart, from those who no longer deserve it.

FIVE "L'S" TO LIVING A
Full Life

HOW DO YOU FEEL?

66

Free yourself from that past hurt. There's a new love waiting for you on the other side of it. However, it starts with identifying the wounds that are still open and giving yourself enough grace to heal, before trying to love anyone else.

FIVE "L'S" TO LIVING A
Full Life

HOW DO YOU FEEL?

"

When you stop expecting them to change and see them for who they are, you'll stop breaking your own heart.

Instead, be with the person who tries their best to do right by you, instead of the person who has perfected their plan to get you back, after they've intentionally hurt you.

HOW DO YOU FEEL?

"

Love is only worth the investment when it is reciprocated.

How many times have you made a deposit and your account came up empty?

HOW DO YOU FEEL?

"

Your heart is a muscle that requires healthy exercise.

What are you doing to strengthen yours?

FIVE "L'S" TO LIVING A
Full Life

HOW DO YOU FEEL?

66

As you grow, what you value will change, but regardless of what changes, making you a priority should not be one of them.

FIVE "L'S" TO LIVING A
Full Life

HOW DO YOU FEEL?

PAGE 55

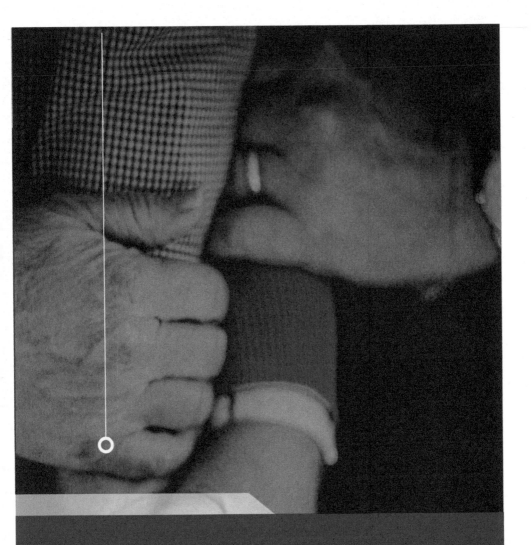

Longevity

Sustainability = Longevity

Without unlearning the lessons that no longer serve you and learning the things that do, you run the risk of limiting your accomplishments which decreases your chances of reaching your greatest potential.

Longevity in your personal and professional life is about the choices that you make and the chances that you take.

Next, is waiting on you

"

You were designed to be great, but if you don't appreciate the blueprint, you'll never build a strong foundation.

FIVE "L'S" TO LIVING A
Full Life

WHAT'S ON YOUR MIND?

66

Your battle is over when you give it to god.
Sometimes when you try to do it
yourself, you tend to get in his way. Learn
the art of patience and move when you
are led to do so.

WHAT'S ON YOUR MIND?

SELF-HELP
Guide

66

Never stop showing up for you. You should
always advocate for the things that you
want, but most importantly, for the things
that you need.

Do you even know the difference?

WHAT'S ON YOUR MIND?

"

If you change the behavior, you'll change your life. However, you can't manifest what you aren't willing to fix, in order to create a better life.

FIVE "L'S" TO LIVING A
Full Life

WHAT'S ON YOUR MIND?

66

What do you want for your life and what are you willing to sacrifice to get it?

WHAT'S ON YOUR MIND?

66

Never be afraid to stand alone, especially when it comes to fighting for your passion and purpose. Everyone may not understand the decisions you make and the risk that you take, but it's not for them to understand. It's for you to finish.

FIVE "L'S" TO LIVING A
Full Life

WHAT'S ON YOUR MIND?

66

When the load gets heavy, you have to ensure that what you're carrying is indeed your weight. Sometimes, we create storms and cry when it rains. Every battle is not yours to fight and when you realize and release it, you'll be able to truly live your best life.

FIVE "L'S" TO LIVING A
Full Life

WHAT'S ON YOUR MIND?

SELF-HELP
Guide

66

Remember that people only do what you
allow. You'll never heal from what has broken
you if you keep allowing the same behavior
to happen. You have to be willing to accept
that the consequences that you face are
from the decisions that you've made.

Have you made choices that you are willing
to stand by despite the repercussions that
may follow?

FIVE "L'S" TO LIVING A
Full Life

WHAT'S ON YOUR MIND?

"

Never miss the lesson!

Along your journey, there will be times of frustration and happiness, but whatever you do, pay attention. Remember how you felt, how hard you worked, and the mistakes that may have been made; those are the teachable moments. Give yourself grace and know that a failure is only someone who never tries.

FIVE "L'S" TO LIVING A
Full Life

WHAT'S ON YOUR MIND?

"

When you are good to yourself, you won't allow anyone to mishandle you. You have to teach people how to treat you, but if you don't know how to treat yourself, how can you expect anyone else to?

FIVE "L'S" TO LIVING A
Full Life

WHAT'S ON YOUR MIND?

Your journey is unique to your passion and purpose. Stop comparing where you are to others and focus. Let them inspire you, not pause you.

FIVE "L'S" TO LIVING A
Full Life

WHAT'S ON YOUR MIND?

66

Sometimes you have to sit still and figure
out what you want for your life.

Write it down!

FIVE "L'S" TO LIVING A
Full Life

WHAT'S ON YOUR MIND?

SELF-HELP
Guide

"

You've cried long enough. Just know that those tears were necessary for the best version of you to grow.

You have been planting seeds in fertile ground for long enough, it is time for you to reap your harvest.

FIVE "L'S" TO LIVING A
Full Life

WHAT'S ON YOUR MIND?

"

Those same bricks that were used to bury you, helped to build the foundation that you now stand on.

Be thankful for the blows, they are the reason why you are still standing.

FIVE "L'S" TO LIVING A
Full Life

WHAT'S ON YOUR MIND?

"

Don't ever be afraid to start over. Sometimes you have to learn the hard lessons, in order to accomplish that major goal.

Do you know the steps that you need to take in order to accomplish your goal?

FIVE "L'S" TO LIVING A
Full Life

WHAT'S ON YOUR MIND?

"

You will never be who you need to be while pretending to be who they want you to be. Stop living in their shadows and find comfort in being the truest version of you.

You deserve the best and it's your responsibility to make sure you have it.

FIVE "L'S" TO LIVING A
Full Life

WHAT'S ON YOUR MIND?

"

Remember that your superpower is not just found in your strength, it is also found in your ability to be human.

That means that it is okay, to not be okay or to not have all of the answers.

Keep going!

FIVE "L'S" TO LIVING A
Full Life

WHAT'S ON YOUR MIND?

Leap

Taking a leap of faith is not always easy. Most of us are so uncomfortably comfortable, that we make every excuse as to why you can't have more.

At some point, you have to remove all doubt and give your goals and your life a fighting chance.

Leap!

That's the only way you'll learn to fly.

66

As you rid yourself of toxic people, make
sure that you release that toxic energy that
is inside of you as well.

How are you going to become a better
person when you are half of the problem?

FIVE "L'S" TO LIVING A
Full Life

WHAT ARE YOU GOING TO DO DIFFERENTLY?

PAGE 95

66

Don't let self-doubt keep you from giving your dreams a fighting chance. Every single time you feel that you are ready, you find a way to talk yourself out of it.

It is time that you replace your fear with faith and keep moving your feet even if you are scared.

FIVE "L'S" TO LIVING A
Full Life

WHAT ARE YOU GOING TO DO DIFFERENTLY?

"

Know that the perfect time will never come. You have to be willing to create it for yourself.

Are you willing to take a chance?

FIVE "L'S" TO LIVING A
Full Life

WHAT ARE YOU GOING TO DO DIFFERENTLY?

"

All that you need to be successful can be found, inside of you. Don't be afraid to explore the wonders within.

WHAT ARE YOU GOING TO DO DIFFERENTLY?

SELF-HELP
Guide

"

Take a step towards becoming a better version of you. Make sure that your attitude, movements, and decisions align with the life that you wish to live.

WHAT ARE YOU GOING TO DO DIFFERENTLY?

"

Get your head in the game. Pay attention to the plays, know your position and be ready when it's your turn to score.

FIVE "L'S" TO LIVING A
Full Life

WHAT ARE YOU GOING TO DO DIFFERENTLY?

"

You'll never accomplish anything if you don't take the first step. Don't let your fear overshadow your faith. Believe in yourself.

WHAT ARE YOU GOING TO DO DIFFERENTLY?

66

Look in the mirror and realize that you have
to take yourself and your needs seriously.

If you don't then who will?

WHAT ARE YOU GOING TO DO DIFFERENTLY?

66

You can accomplish anything that you put your mind to doing. You just have to be willing to fight for it.

Are you ready?

WHAT ARE YOU GOING TO DO DIFFERENTLY?

66

Don't just chase the dream; chase the happiness that goes along with it.

The money and status are great, but the love for what you do is even better.

WHAT ARE YOU GOING TO DO DIFFERENTLY?

66

While you are on this road to self-discovery, know that the weight may get heavy, the attacks may get stronger, but the reward will make it all worth it.

Keep going!

FIVE "L'S" TO LIVING A
Full Life

WHAT ARE YOU GOING TO DO DIFFERENTLY?

Letting Go

Holding on to your past can be a gift and a curse. It's a gift because it is a reminder of just how far you've come, but it can also be a curse filled with the trauma, doubt, and fear that you have carried your entire life.

66

It is time to take control of your life, confront the blemishes of your past, heal and let it go.

Welcome to the first day of the rest of your life!

FIVE "L'S" TO LIVING A
Full Life

HOW ARE YOU GOING TO SET YOURSELF FREE?

66

Be mindful of the people who are desperate to fit in. If push came to shove, they'll never stand on principle, but always popular opinion.

FIVE "L'S" TO LIVING A
Full Life

HOW ARE YOU GOING TO SET YOURSELF FREE?

66

Your circle is a reflection of you. Now, look in the mirror and tell me if you like what you see?

FIVE "L'S" TO LIVING A
Full Life

HOW ARE YOU GOING TO SET YOURSELF FREE?

66

Don't let your temporary emotions make permanent decisions in your life. You do not want to wake one morning and regret a decision that you made simply because you weren't in the best headspace.

Give yourself time to process how you feel before determining your next call to action.

Remember that cooler heads prevail.

FIVE "L'S" TO LIVING A
Full Life

HOW ARE YOU GOING TO SET YOURSELF FREE?

66

Don't allow your past experiences to hinder you from trying again. Let your past be a reminder of how you've overcome, instead of being a crutch, keeping you from your future.

It is time to stop carrying that weight as a badge of honor and truly find peace in the release.

FIVE "L'S" TO LIVING A
Full Life

HOW ARE YOU GOING TO SET YOURSELF FREE?

66

Don't let anyone tell you that because of who you were and the mistakes that you've made, that your life is over. You have the ability to make a positive change and impact in your life and community.

It starts with making a decision and standing on your word.

Be thankful for your past but allow your focus to be on your future.

It is your time!

FIVE "L'S" TO LIVING A
Full Life

HOW ARE YOU GOING TO SET YOURSELF FREE?

66

Avoid people whose goal in life is to constantly highlight and provoke the ugly that lives inside of you.

If every single time you are around them, they say or do something to trigger you... Then they are not in support of you.

Do not equate history with happiness.

It is time to let go!

FIVE "L'S" TO LIVING A
Full Life

HOW ARE YOU GOING TO SET YOURSELF FREE?

"

Stop seeking validation from the very person that broke you.

Why would they ever support you on your journey to greater?

HOW ARE YOU GOING TO SET YOURSELF FREE?

"

Never let the opinion of others determine your worth.

Remember that hurt people, hurt people... And if they don't value themselves, they'll never value you.

It is your job to remember who you are.

Regardless of what anyone says, never be afraid to stand in your greatness.

FIVE "L'S" TO LIVING A
Full Life

HOW ARE YOU GOING TO SET YOURSELF FREE?

66

How much longer are you going to make excuses? How much longer are you going to blame others for the opportunities that you've missed?

It is time for you to let all of the self-doubt, fear of defeat, and anger go. It is time for you to do what you know needs to be done. It is time for you to let your light shine.

FIVE "L'S" TO LIVING A
Full Life

HOW ARE YOU GOING TO SET YOURSELF FREE?

66

Stop holding on to what was and see things
for how they truly are; you may save yourself
a lifetime of pain.

What Are You Afraid Of?

FIVE "L'S" TO LIVING A
Full Life

HOW ARE YOU GOING TO SET YOURSELF FREE?

SELF-HELP
Guide

"

You've let them tell you who you were for years. You've lived in their shadow and feared drawing outside of the lines. You've watch as your true self fade into the background, just to make them happy.

Well, enough is enough.

It is time for you to be true to yourself and become who you were created to be.

Don't you miss you?

FIVE "L'S" TO LIVING A
Full Life

HOW ARE YOU GOING TO SET YOURSELF FREE?

66

Don't even start your day with that worry and stress. Leave that energy outside...It can't afford to go with you.

Speak like into your day and make a decision to speak to every mountain that may have formed and command it to move.

You have the power to make your day what it needs to be....

So what do you choose today?

FIVE "L'S" TO LIVING A
Full Life

HOW ARE YOU GOING TO SET YOURSELF FREE?

SELF-HELP
Guide

66

Don't even start your day with that worry and stress. Leave that energy outside...It can't afford to go with you.

Speak like into your day and make a decision to speak to every mountain that may have formed and command it to move.

You have the power to make your day what it needs to be....

So what do you choose today?

FIVE "L'S" TO LIVING A
Full Life

HOW ARE YOU GOING TO SET YOURSELF FREE?

SELF-HELP
Guide

"

Stop trying to convince people of what you bring to the table, and just stop eating with them.

Anyone interested in what you have to offer will bring their plates, but don't ever lower your standards and starve just to please them.

Are you hungry?

FIVE "L'S" TO LIVING A
Full Life

HOW ARE YOU GOING TO SET YOURSELF FREE?

66

Wait until you see what is on the other side
of your struggle!

Right now it's hard to see the sun through
the rain, but you have to remember that it
doesn't rain forever and that the sun will
shine again.

Know that nothing grows without water and
sunlight; these tough times are necessary.

It's okay to give in, but don't you ever give
up!

FIVE "L'S" TO LIVING A
Full Life

HOW ARE YOU GOING TO SET YOURSELF FREE?

"

It is time to regain control over your life. You have been making emotional decisions for long enough and it's time to show up in your greatness.

Answer this question, how much more of your happiness are you willing to give away?

FIVE "L'S" TO LIVING A
Full Life

HOW ARE YOU GOING TO SET YOURSELF FREE?

As you've gone through this journey, you've made promises and declarations to yourself. For the first time, in a very long time, you have faced your fears, confronted your past, laughed at your mistakes, and found yourself right where you need to be to take the next step in becoming the best version of yourself.

You should be proud of yourself. You did the work but it's not over. You have to remain consistent and you have to take every single day and live it out loud... but for you this time.

You have the power to rid yourself of any/all toxicity that has been wreaking havoc in your life.

This is your song now, set the tempo!

Just know that if you're ever in need of support, I am here.... Screaming from the stands, insisting that you keep going, simply because i believe in you.

Now, it's time that you believe in yourself too.

Welcome to phase six.... We'll call this one......

Leveling up!!!!

Coach key

Made in the USA
Columbia, SC
30 June 2022

62528101R00085